Information for Parents

In literacy lessons teachers will be seeking to encourage their pupils to:

- Read confidently and with understanding;
- Understand phonics and spelling patterns;
- Use neat handwriting with speed and accuracy;
- Expand their vocabulary;
- Appreciate a range of styles in fiction and poetry;
- Understand how stories are structured by the writers' use of settings, characters and plots;
- Read and use non-fiction materials;
- Develop their own writing using techniques of planning, drafting and editing;
- Enjoy reading books;
- Use imagination and inventiveness in their own writing.

Throughout the primary years the children will address their literacy work at three levels: word level, sentence level and text level.

Word level work includes word recognition, phonics, spelling, vocabulary and handwriting.

Sentence level work covers grammatical awareness, sentence construction and punctuation.

Text level work covers comprehension of reading and the composition of writing. It includes working with fiction, non-fiction and poetry.

Many schools operate a 'literacy hour' where they address all the aspects of literacy directly, but they will also seek to cover some aspects through other subjects throughout the school day.

In the **Literacy Now** series we provide practice materials for word level, sentence level and text level work, matched appropriately to children's ages. The books are designed to be used by parents working with their children to provide extra practice, whether out of a need to improve particular aspects of the children's progress or simply for the fun of working on English at home.

Literacy Now
for ages 10–11

Excellent practice for literacy

You may prefer to use this book as a textbook, rather than as a book to write in. If so, you will need to use an exercise book for your answers.

Try to work out the type of answer that is required for each question. Some questions just need single words for their answers; others need whole sentences. We sometimes provide two or more lines to write answers on, to give you clues as to how much you ought to write.

If you need help from an adult it is all right to ask for it. Sometimes you can learn a lot more just by having a small amount of help. It is always a good idea to have your worked checked by an adult when you have finished it. If you have made mistakes you can learn from them.

Andrew Brodie

The Secret Garden

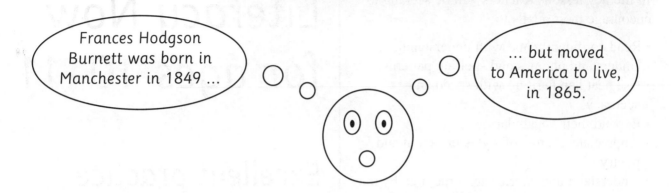

Frances Hodgson Burnett was born in Manchester in 1849 ...

... but moved to America to live, in 1865.

The text below is from 'The Secret Garden', written by Francis Hodgson Burnett. This extract is taken from the first chapter of the novel. The chapter tells of how the young girl, Mary, lived with her parents in India before they died.

Mary was standing in the middle of the nursery when they opened the door a few minutes later. She looked an ugly, cross little thing and was frowning because she was beginning to be hungry and feel disgracefully neglected. The first man who came in was a large officer she had once seen talking to her father. He looked tired and troubled, but when he saw her he was so startled that he almost jumped back.

'Barney!' he cried out. 'There is a child in here! A child alone! In a place like this! Mercy on us, who is she?'

'I am Mary Lennox,' the little girl said, drawing herself up stiffly. She thought the man was very rude to call her father's bungalow 'a place like this'. 'I fell asleep when everyone had the cholera and I have only just wakened up. Why does nobody come?'

'It is the child no one ever saw!' exclaimed the man, turning to his companions. 'She has actually been forgotten!'

'Why was I forgotten?' Mary said, stamping her foot. 'Why does nobody come?'

The young man whose name was Barney looked at her very sadly. Mary even thought she saw him wink his eyes as if to wink tears away.

'Poor little kid!' he said. 'There is nobody left to come.'

It was in that strange and sudden way that Mary found out that she had neither father nor mother left; and they had died and been carried away in the night, and that the few native servants who had not died also had left the house as quickly as they could get out of it, none of them even remembering that there was a missie sahib. That was why the place was so quiet. It was true that there was no one in the bungalow but herself and the little rustling snake.

The Secret Garden

1 Was Mary an attractive child? Explain your answer.

_____

_____

2 Why does one of the men refer to the bungalow as 'a place like this'?

_____

_____

3 How do we know that Mary is cross at having been forgotten?

_____

_____

4 How had Mary's parents died? _____

_____

5 Who or what had been Mary's only companion in the bungalow shortly before the two men arrived?

_____

Prefixes

prefix	meaning
aero	air
bi	two
micro	small

Choose one of these three prefixes to make new words.

_____ drome

_____ ped

_____ scopic

_____ dynamic

_____ phone

_____ batics

_____ noculars

_____ processor

_____ cycle

_____ lateral

_____ chip

_____ sol

Treasure Island

 The extract below is from 'Treasure Island' by Robert Louis Stevenson.

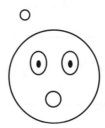 This novel, written in the 19th century, is about a cabin boy called Jim. It involves pirates and, of course, treasure.

Jim, who is to be the new cabin boy, is sent on an errand ...

When I had done breakfasting the squire gave me a note addressed to John Silver, at the sign of 'The Spyglass', and told me I should easily find the place by following the line of the docks, and keeping a bright look-out for a little tavern with a large brass telescope for a sign.

I set off, overjoyed at this opportunity to see some more of the ships and seamen, and picked my way among a great crowd of people and carts and bales, for the dock was now at its busiest, until I found the tavern in question.

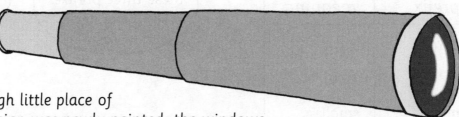

It was a bright enough little place of entertainment. The sign was newly painted; the windows had neat red curtains; the floor was cleanly sanded. There was a street on either side, and an open door on both, which made the large, low room pretty clear to see in, in spite of clouds of tobacco smoke.

The customers were mostly seafaring men; and they talked so loudly that I hung at the door, almost afraid to enter.

1 Who is meant by 'I' in the text? _____

2 What is meant by a 'spyglass'? _____

Treasure Island

3 Choose from below the word closest in meaning to 'tavern'.

hotel   office   pub   shop   mansion

4 What type of people were the main customers at 'The Spyglass'?

_____

_____

5 Who was Jim sent to take a note to?

_____

_____

6 Was Jim happy to be sent on this errand?
Use the text to explain your answer.

_____

_____

_____

Suffixes

Add one of the four given suffixes to make new words.

suffix	meaning
phobia	fear
ology	study/knowledge
scope	view/see
clude	shut

con _____   arachno _____   bi _____

agora _____   ex _____   tele _____

micro _____   claustro _____   peri _____

Black Beauty

The text is taken from the story of 'Black Beauty', which was written in the 19th century by Anna Sewell.

The book is about a horse called Black Beauty. The extract is taken from the early part of the story, whilst Black Beauty is still young.

I must not forget to mention one part of my training which I have always considered a very great advantage. My master sent me for a fortnight to a neighbouring farmer who had a meadow which was skirted on one side by the railway. Here were some sheep and cows, and I was turned in amongst them.

I shall never forget the first train that ran by. I was feeding quietly near the pales which separated the meadow from the railway, when I heard a strange sound at a distance; and before I knew whence it came – with a rush and a clatter, and a puffing out of smoke – a long black train of something flew by, and was gone almost before I could draw my breath. I turned, and galloped to the further side of the meadow as fast as I could go; and there I stood snorting with astonishment and fear.

In the course of the day many other trains went by, some more slowly; these drew up at the station close by, and sometimes made an awful shriek and groan before they stopped. I thought it very dreadful, but the cows went on eating very quietly, and hardly raised their heads as the black, frightful thing came puffing and grinding past.

For the first few days I could not feed at peace; but as I found that this terrible creature never came into the field nor did me any harm, I began to disregard it; and very soon I cared as little about the passing of a train as the cows and sheep did.

Black Beauty

1 Who is meant by 'I' in the text? _____

2 For how many weeks was Black Beauty sent to a neighbouring farmer?

_____

3 With whom did he share the meadow? _____

4 What ran by one edge of the meadow? _____

5 In the last paragraph, as what does Black Beauty describe the train?

_____

6 How did Black Beauty react to the first train that passed the meadow?

_____

_____

7 Explain why Black Beauty might consider this fortnight in the meadows as a 'very great advantage'.

_____

_____

Tricky spellings

Each of the answers to the clues is a word that can be tricky to spell.
A few letters have been put in to help you.

1. Something very small.   m _ n _ _ t _ re

2. Second month of the year.   F _ _ _ _ _ _ y

3. The study of places.   g _ _ g _ _ ph _

4. A soft summer fruit.   r _ _ _ _ erry

5. A name, perhaps at the end of a letter.   s _ _ nat _ _ _

6. The day after Tuesday.   W _ _ _ _ _ day

Literacy terminology

Choose words from the box to complete the puzzle below.

singular   half-rhyme   noun
clause   tense   adverb
fable   consonant   synonym
genre   syllables   onomatopoeia
paragraph   simile

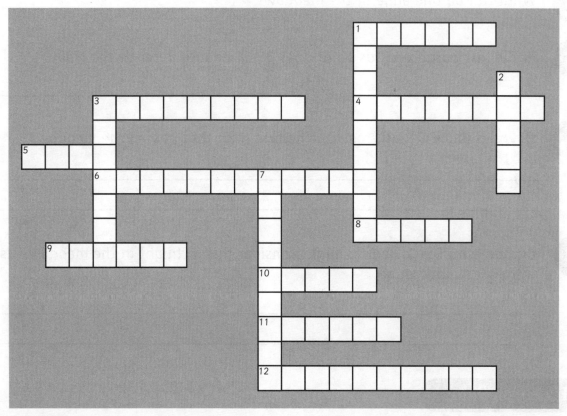

Clues Across

1. Part of a sentence including a verb.
3. The 'beats' or separate sounds in a word.
4. Just <u>one</u>.
5. A naming word.
6. Words that sound like their meaning, e.g. hiss
8. This denotes when something happens (past, present or future).
9. A figure of speech that likens something to another thing to create imagery, e.g. 'a face like thunder'.
10. A type of writing, e.g. drama, mystery, science fiction etc.
11. A word used to describe a verb.
12. Words that nearly rhyme.

Clues Down

1. A letter that is not a vowel.
2. A story with a moral lesson.
3. A word with the same or similar meaning as another word.
7. A group of sentences on the same subject.

8

Words old and new

Take the words from the box below and sort them into those that have been in common use in our language for more than a hundred years and those that have been in everyday use in our language for less than a hundred years.

> Royal Air Force   hovercraft
> cavalry   ship   trainers   shoes
> book   supersonic   electronics
> cart   internet   horse

Old words   New words

_____   _____

_____   _____

_____   _____

_____   _____

_____   _____

_____   _____

Can you think of any other words that are new?

_____   _____

_____   _____

Robinson Crusoe

This text is taken from the story 'Robinson Crusoe'.

It was written by Daniel Defoe and first published in 1719.

In the text below, the young sailor is on his first voyage when his ship is caught in a storm off the coast of Norfolk.

But the worst was not come yet; the storm continued with such a fury, that the seamen themselves acknowledged they had never known a worse. We had a good ship, but she was deep loaden, and wallowed in the sea, that the seamen every now and then cried out she would founder.

It was my advantage, in one respect, that I did not know what they meant by founder till I inquired. However, the storm was so violent, that I saw what is not often seen, the master, the boatswain, and some others more sensible than the rest, at their prayers, and expecting every moment when the ship would go to the bottom.

In the middle of the night, and under all the rest of our distresses, one of the men that had been down on purpose to see, cried out we had sprung a leak, another said there was a four foot of water in the hold. Then all hands were called to the pump.

Now answer the questions.

1   Explain the words 'she was deep loaden'. _____

   _____

2   Why did the author think that it was to his advantage that he did not at first understand the word 'founder'?

   _____

   _____

3 How did he find out the meaning of 'founder'?
(Use your own words, don't just copy the text.)

_____

4 At what time was a leak discovered?

_____

5 Explain the sentence 'Then all hands were called to the pump'.

_____

_____

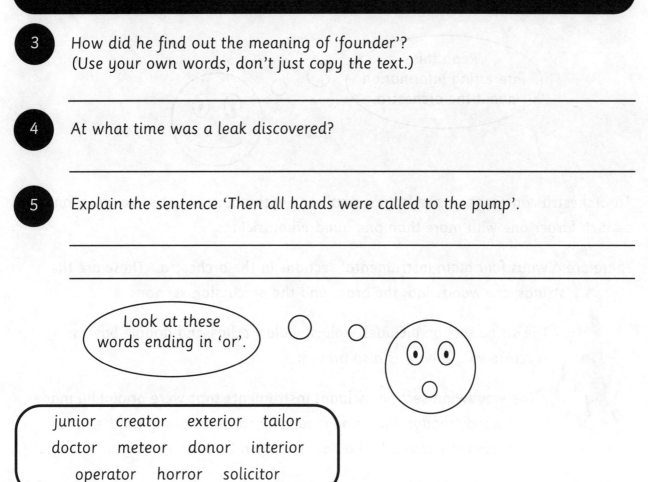

Look at these words ending in 'or'.

junior   creator   exterior   tailor
doctor   meteor   donor   interior
operator   horror   solicitor

The answer to each clue is a word ending in 'or' from the box. The letters in the shaded squares should give you another 'or' word found on a farm!

1. Shooting star

2. Maker

3. Makes suits

4. Lawyer

5. Outside

6. Giver

7. Inside

A _____ is found on a farm!

Now write the leftover 'or' words from the box.

_____   _____   _____   _____

Marvellous music

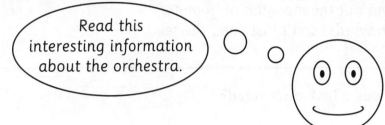

Read this interesting information about the orchestra.

An orchestra can range in size from a small one with about twenty-five musicians to a much larger one with more than one hundred musicians.

There are always four main instrumental sections in the orchestra. These are the strings, the woodwind, the brass and the percussion sections.

The string section includes violins, violas, cellos and double basses; occasionally a harp is also present.

The woodwind section includes instruments that were originally made of wood (though the same modern instruments may not be) and make their sound by having air blown through them.

The brass section is where the brass instruments can be found; these would usually include trumpets, trombones and tubas, amongst others.

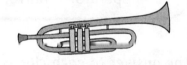

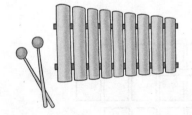

Lastly, the percussion section has those instruments that are struck to produce their sounds and would include untuned instruments, such as drums, and tuned percussion, such as xylophones.

The only person in the orchestra who does not play an instrument is the conductor. His role is to lead the orchestra, ensuring that the members play their music at the right time and volume.

A good conductor is essential to a successful orchestra and the players are seated in a semicircular arrangement so that they all have a good view of their leader.

Marvellous music

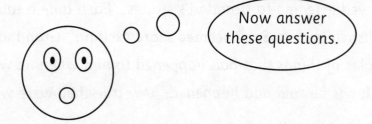

Now answer these questions.

1 Could you have an orchestra of around sixty musicians? Explain how you know this.
_____
_____
_____

2 Name the sections of the orchestra.
_____
_____
_____
_____

3 The flute would be found in the woodwind section of the orchestra, even though it is made of metal. Explain why this is.
_____
_____
_____

4 In which section of the orchestra would you find the triangle? Explain how you know this.
_____
_____
_____

5 Name the only member of the orchestra that does not play an instrument.
_____

6 In the last sentence of the text, who is meant by 'their leader'?
_____
_____

Grandad's stories

Sam loved listening to Grandad's stories. Each time a tale was told it became more embellished and, to Sam, seemed more exciting. Grandad particularly liked to tell Sam tales of things that had happened to him when he was a young man. Or at least things he said had happened; how true they were was a matter for debate.

If he was to be believed, Grandad had probably been some sort of secret agent. Often in a story the words 'double 'o' eight' slipped out, though Sam thought Grandad could quite probably be Superman himself.

Mum said that he shouldn't take too much notice of Grandad's stories as he was very old and sometimes became confused. However, Sam enjoyed hearing about how Grandad had foiled an attempt to flood the country with counterfeit money, how he had worked with heads of state and police forces around the world to keep people safe and how he had outwitted master criminals.

It didn't matter to Sam what anyone else believed, he knew in his heart that Grandad's stories were based in reality and he looked forward each week to visiting Grandad on Saturday morning and hearing more about his exciting life.

Grandad's stories

Now answer these questions.

1 Why did Sam particularly enjoy listening to Grandad's stories?

_____

_____

2 What is meant by the term 'heads of state'?

_____

3 Why did Mum think Sam shouldn't completely believe all Grandad's stories?

_____

_____

4 Did Sam believe the stories? Explain your answer.

_____

_____

_____

You may need a dictionary to help you now.

Write a simple definition for each of the following words. The words can all be found in the text.

embellished _____

debate _____

foiled _____

counterfeit _____

outwitted _____

reality _____

15

I Wandered Lonely as a Cloud

I WANDERED LONELY AS A CLOUD

I wandered lonely as a cloud
That floats on high o'er vales and hills,
When all at once I saw a crowd,
A host, of golden daffodils;
Beside the lake, beneath the trees,
Fluttering and dancing in the breeze.

Continuous as the stars that shine
And twinkle on the milky way,
They stretched in never-ending line
Along the margin of a bay:
Ten thousand saw I at a glance,
Tossing their heads in sprightly dance.

The waves beside them danced; but they
outdid the sparkling waves in glee:
A poet could not but be gay,
In such a jocund company:
I gazed – and gazed – but little thought
What wealth the show to me had brought.

For oft, when on my couch I lie
In vacant or in pensive mood,
They flash upon that inward eye
Which is the bliss of solitude;
And then my heart with pleasure fills
And dances with the daffodils.

I Wandered Lonely as a Cloud

1 Write the title of the poem.

_____

2 Name the author. _____

3 How do we know in the first verse that the poet was alone?

_____

_____

4 What did he see beside the lake, beneath the trees? _____

5 What number did he choose to describe the amount he thought he saw?

_____

6 What does the poet mean by the following words:

vales (verse 1)	_____	glee (verse 3)	_____
o'er (verse 1)	_____	jocund (verse 3)	_____
margin (verse 2)	_____	oft (verse 4)	_____
sprightly (verse 2)	_____	pensive (verse 4)	_____

7 What is meant by 'the inward eye' (verse 4)?

_____

_____

Prefixes

bi = two   **tri = three**   **quad = four**

The answer to each of the clues begins with one of the prefixes above.
Use a dictionary to ensure you spell each answer correctly.

This form of transport has pedals and two wheels.   _____

An animal that uses all four of its feet to walk.   _____

Three-sided shape.   _____

A three-legged camera stand.   _____

Glasses aiding near and distant vision.   _____

A quarter of a circle.   _____

Clouds

We are all familiar with clouds. They can be seen in the sky on most days. Even the brightest of days, with a seemingly clear blue sky, often has odd little cotton wool looking clouds appearing from time to time.

There are many different types of cloud, so for convenience of identification they are categorized into ten different sorts. These are variations on the three main types; cumulus clouds (the fluffy looking ones), stratus clouds (those formed in layers) and cirrus (the feathery or herringbone looking clouds).

Different types of cloud are found at different heights above sea level, and cloud names that include the word 'nimbus' usually bring rain.

The full range of cloud types beginning from these found at the highest altitude and working downwards are:

Cirrus, Cirrostratus, Cirrocumulus, Altostratus, Altocumulus, Stratocumulus, Cumulus, Cumulonimbus, Stratus and Nimbostratus.

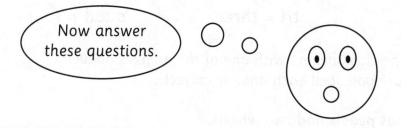

Now answer these questions.

1 The author begins this text with the words, 'We are all familiar with clouds'. Is this statement fact or opinion?

_____

2 What are often found in a sky that seems clear?

_____

Clouds

3 Name the three main types of cloud.

_____   _____   _____

4 Name two sorts of cloud that might result in rain.

_____   _____

5 Name a type of cloud that would be very low in the sky.

_____

6 What sort of cloud might be found at the highest altitude?

_____

Weather sayings

Explain each of these well-known weather sayings.

7 Raining cats and dogs.

_____

_____

8 Red sky at night, shepherd's delight.
Red sky in the morning shepherd's warning.

_____

_____

9 Oak before Ash, in for a splash.
Ash before Oak, in for a soak.

_____

_____

The thirsty crow

Here is a modern version of one of the famous Aesop's Fables.

It was a hot summer day and Crow was very thirsty. At first he could find no water anywhere, but eventually he saw a little fresh water glistening in the bottom of a watering can.

He was very frustrated to discover that the water was too far down the can for him to reach it. After some thought he began to pick up pieces of shingle from the garden path and drop them one at a time into the can.

Eventually, by doing this, he had made the water level rise high enough to enable him to have a drink.

He flew away refreshed and happy.

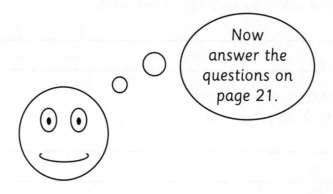

Now answer the questions on page 21.

The thirsty crow

1 At what time of year did this story take place? _____

2 Who was the original 'teller' of this tale? _____

3 Which of the following is the lesson learned from this tale.
(Ring the correct answer)

    Look before you leap.   Slow and steady wins the race.

    Necessity is the master of invention.   Pride comes before a fall.

4 Explain how dropping pieces of shingle into the water made the water
level rise.

_____

_____

_____

5 Write a simple definition for each of the following words from the text.

You may need to use a dictionary.

shingle   _____

eventually _____

glistening _____

refreshed _____

fable   _____

version   _____

frustrated _____

Spelling

In this short text there are many spelling errors. See if you can spot them as you are reading.

You may need to use a dictionary.

Anne went into the lownge. She closed the curtins as it was beginning to get dark.
She then sat down to wach a film that had just started on the televistuin. A moment later there was a nock on the dore. It was Anne's best freind Kelly.

The two girsls sat down and thorouly engoyed the film.

When the film had ended, Anne and Kelly helped one another with there maths homework. It was a tricky task and included work on paralel lines, quadrillaterells and equalateral triangles. The girls took nearly an hour to complete the work.

At twenty past nine Kelly sed goodbye and left, as she had to be home by nine thirty.

Now underline the fifteen incorrect spellings with a coloured pen or pencil.

Use the lines below to rewrite the words correctly.

_____   _____   _____

_____   _____   _____

_____   _____   _____

_____   _____   _____

_____   _____   _____

Spelling

Look at the following words. There are five pairs of homophones.

Next to the first word in each pair is a definition. Your job is to write a definition for the second word in each pair.

Brighton   a coastal town in the south of England.

brighten   _____

_____

stationary   not moving.

stationery   _____

_____

dew   small drops of water; often forms on grass overnight.

due   _____

_____

mite   a very small creature.

might   _____

_____

lesson   a period of learning.

lessen   _____

_____

The Railway Children (part 1)

The text below is from the novel 'The Railway Children' by E. Nesbit.

In this extract the three children, Peter, Bobbie (short for Roberta) and Phyllis, have just moved into a house called 'Three Chimneys' with their mother.

They had not been a week at Three Chimneys before they had asked Mother to let them have a piece of garden each for their very own, and she had agreed, and the south border under the peach trees had been divided into three pieces and they were allowed to plant whatever they liked there.

Phyllis had planted mignonette and nasturtium and Virginia Stock in hers. The seeds came up and though they looked just like weeds, Phyllis believed that they would bear flowers someday. The Virginia Stock justified her faith quite soon, and her garden was gay with a band of bright little flowers, pink and white and red and mauve.

'I can't weed for fear I pull up the wrong things,' she used to say comfortably; 'it saves such a lot of work.'

Peter sowed vegetable seeds in his – carrots and onions and turnips. The seed was given to him by the farmer who lived in the nice black-and-white, wood-and-plaster house just beyond the bridge. He kept turkeys and guinea fowls, and was a most amiable man. But Peter's vegetables never had much of a chance, because he liked to use the earth of his garden for digging canals, and making forts and earthworks for his toy soldiers. And the seeds of vegetables rarely come to much in a soil that is constantly disturbed for the purposes of war and irrigation.

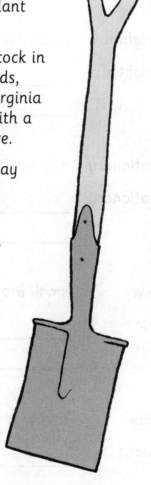

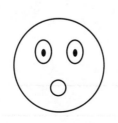

Now answer the questions on page 25.

The Railway Children (part 1)

1 What was the house called? _____

2 What was growing by the area that was to be used for the children's gardening? _____

3 Name three types of plant that Phyllis put in her section of the garden.

_____ _____ _____

4 Which of these soon flowered? _____

5 What excuse did Phyllis use to ensure she did very little work in the garden?

_____

_____

6 Who gave Peter vegetable seed for his section of the garden?

_____

_____

7 What does 'sowed' mean in the phrase 'Peter sowed vegetable seeds'?

_____

8 Why didn't Peter's seeds produce a crop of vegetables?

_____

_____

9 Explain what is meant by 'war and irrigation'.

_____

_____

10 Why has the author written this text in four clear paragraphs? Explain your answer fully.

_____

_____

_____

_____

The Railway Children (part 2)

This extract from the novel follows immediately on from the one on page 24.
Another character, Perks, is introduced – he is the local station porter.

Bobbie planted rose-bushes in her garden, but all the little new leaves of the rose-bushes shrivelled and withered, perhaps because she moved them from the other part of the garden in May, which is not at all the right time of year for moving roses. But she would not own that they were dead, and hoped on against hope, until the day when Perks came up to see the garden, and told her quite plainly that all her roses were as dead as door nails.

'Only good for bonfires, Miss,' he said. 'You just dig 'em up and burn 'em, and I'll give you some nice fresh roots outer my garden; pansies, and stocks, and sweet williams, and forget-me-nots. I'll bring 'em along tomorrow if you get the ground ready.'

So next day she set to work, and that happened to be the day when Mother had praised her and the others about not quarrelling.

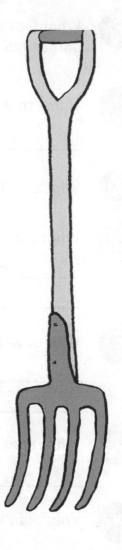

Now answer the questions.

1 Why might Bobbie's rose-bushes not have thrived?

_____

_____

2 What state of health did Perks say the rose-bushes were in and what did he advise Bobbie to do with them?

_____

_____

The Railway Children (part 2)

3 In what way did Perks offer to help Bobbie?

_____

_____

4 What did she have to do to be ready for this?

_____

_____

5 When did she do this?

_____

_____

Prefixes

'Con' is a prefix meaning 'with'.

It comes from Latin.

Choose five of the 'con' words from the box to match the clues.

> concern   connect   consent
> contempt   constabulary
> continental   conga
> construct   consequence

Make or build   _____

Give permission   _____

Worry   _____

A long 'snake like' dance   _____

Join together   _____

The Railway Children (part 3)

This text is taken from the same chapter of the book as the previous two extracts. It begins when Bobbie and Peter are arguing over the use of the garden rake, which they both need at the same time.

'I wish I'd had a brother instead of two whiny little kiddy sisters,' said Peter. This was always recognised as indicating the high-water mark of Peter's rage.

Bobbie made the reply she always made to it. 'I can't think why little boys were ever invented,' and just as she said it she looked up, and saw the three long windows of Mother's workshop flashing in the red rays of the sun. The sight brought back those words of praise – 'You don't quarrel like you used to do.'

'Oh!' cried Bobbie, just as if she had been hit, or had caught her finger in a door, or had felt the hideous sharp beginnings of toothache.

'What's the matter?' said Phyllis.

Bobbie wanted to say: 'Don't let's quarrel. Mother hates it so,' but though she tried hard, she couldn't. Peter was looking too disagreeable and insulting.

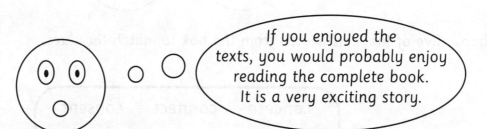

If you enjoyed the texts, you would probably enjoy reading the complete book. It is a very exciting story.

Now answer these questions.

1 Why are the children quarrelling?

_____

_____

2 Explain what is meant by 'the high-water mark of Peter's rage'?

_____

_____

The Railway Children (part 3)

3 Why did Bobbie cry 'Oh!'?

_____

_____

4 Why, at that point, did Bobbie not stop arguing?

_____

_____

5 Where was Mother while the argument was starting?

_____

_____

6 What leads us to believe this?

_____

_____

Prefixes

The prefix 'dec' means 10 ...

... and 'cent' means 100.

Join each clue to the __correct__ word.

100 years	decimetre
A ten sided shape	century
10 centimetres	decade
A type of many legged minibeast	centenarian
10 years	centipede
A person aged 100 years or more	decagon

Looking-glass River

This poem was written by Robert Louis Stevenson.

LOOKING-GLASS RIVER

Smooth it slides upon its travel,
Here a wimple, there a gleam –
O the clean gravel!
O the smooth stream!

Sailing blossoms, silver fishes,
Paven pools as clear as air –
How a child wishes
To live down there!

We can see our coloured faces
Floating on the shaken pool,
Down in cool places,
Dim and very cool;

Till a wind or water wrinkle,
Dipping marten, plumping trout,
Spreads in a twinkle
And blots all out.

See the rings pursue each other;
All below grows black as night,
Just as if mother
Had blown out the light!

Patience, children, just a minute –
See the spreading circles die;
The stream and all in it
Will clear by-and-by.

Looking-glass River

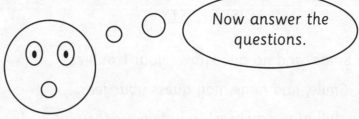

Now answer the questions.

1 What is meant by a 'looking glass'? _____

2 In the first verse how do you know the river is clear and clean?

_____

_____

3 Explain in your own words what happens in verse 4.

_____

_____

_____

_____

4 What is meant in verse 5 by 'see the rings pursue each other'?

_____

_____

_____

5 What is explained at the end of the poem?

_____

_____

_____

'our'

The letter string 'our' occurs in many words.
Learn to spell these tricky 'our' words by covering
them and writing them from memory.

harbour	court	armour	flourish
_____	_____	_____	_____
encourage	scour	tournament	courgette
_____	_____	_____	_____

Dishonesty

DISHONESTY

Smile, and no one knows your troubles,
Smile, and none may guess your fears.
Be 'full of good cheer' to hide your sorrows,
Laugh to shield the growing hurt.

Be cheery, to disguise your pain,
A joke may conceal the ache.
Their lives seem so good, but how would I know?
Their smiles may protect them too.

1 Why do you think the poem is entitled <u>Dishonesty</u>?

_____

_____

_____

2 Explain, as fully as you can, why this writing is clearly a poem rather than prose.

_____

_____

_____

3 Why does the central character of the poem present a happy facade to the world?

_____

_____

_____

4 What does the central character realise in the final two lines?

_____

_____

_____